EARLY ACTIVITY OF

Labelled by three members of the U.S. Geological Survey Volcano Hazards Evaluation Team in a published article in 1975 as overdue for an eruption and likely to do so soon, Mount St. Helens began its eruptive process on March 20, 1980. At 3:47 pm on that date, an earthquake registering 4.1 on the Richter scale shook the area around the mountain. Thought at first to be centered 18 miles to the northeast, the earthquake did not draw much attention. As the frequency of the tremors in the area increased each day, a reexamination of the first quake showed that its location was centered directly under the volcano. Suddenly, Mount St. Helens was beginning to attract attention. One week to the day from the first sign of activity Mount St. Helens began puffing steam and ash, clearing her throat, as it were, for what was to come.

This first eruption and the other early eruptions that followed were steam bursts which occurred when heat from the molten magma far beneath the mountain came in contact with water in the ground. The ash that fell out of these steam plumes was ash that was left deposited in the mountain from the last time the volcano erupted, 123 years before. The early eruptions varied in size and ash content, some plumes reaching heights of more than a mile above the mountain.

From March 27 until the mountain quieted in late April the periodic steam eruptions continued, each one expanding the crater until at the end of April the crater measured roughly 1000 feet by 1500 feet, at its maximum depth it measured 800 feet from the higher south summit to the bottom — deep enough to hold an 80 story building and large enough to accommodate nearly 25 football fields. As the growth of the crater continued through April the frequency of earthquakes around the

MOUNT ST. HELENS

mountain decreased, although the number of tremors in excess of magnitude 4.0 increased. This fact combined with the fact that the mountain had ceased its steam eruptions and that a bulge on the north face of the mountain was expanding at a rate of 5 feet per day gave little clue as to what would happen next. The answer came on the morning of May 18.

MAY 18, 1980

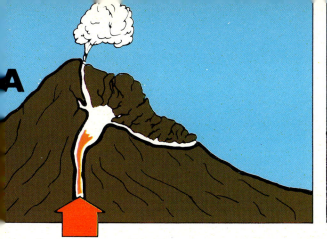

SEQUENCE OF THE MAJOR ERUPTION

A) At 8:30 and again at 8:32 seismographs record earthquakes of magnitude 5.0 or above shaking the mountain. The north face, already weakening and bulging from the pressure of the magma pushing upward, gives way and begins to avalanche down.

B) Free of the weight of the mountain to contain it, the sublimated gases inside the magma were free to expand; like a shaken champagne bottle with its cork removed, a lateral burst results, focused to the north by the intact west, south and east walls of the crater.

C) The eruption reaches a peak in a chain reaction. The more magma released, the less the pressure further down in the magma chamber allowing even a greater rush of gas to escape. Pyroclastic flows, a mixture of super heated gases and other Volcanic material (ash, cinder, pumice) spill out of the lowered north lip of the crater and descend on Spirit Lake at speeds up to 200 mph.

TOTAL DEVASTATION FROM FIRE, FLOODS, MUD AND ASH

It is estimated that 140,000 acre feet of water was thawed out within hours by the heat of the volcano.

This water, combined with an estimated 25 million cubic yards of mud and ash produced mudflows that scoured out the North and South Forks of the Toutle River to the Northwest of the Mountain, carrying downstream trees, homes, logging equipment, bridges, and anything else along the way. The destructive force of these mudflows continued down the Toutle River to the Cowlitz River, reaching the Columbia River at Longview, 35 miles from the mountain, leaving behind flooded homes, farms and river beds filled with volcanic debris. A large portion of the ash and mud was deposited in the shipping channel of the Columbia River, halting ocean going traffic from the ports of Longview, Vancouver and Portland.

FALLOUT THROUGHOUT THE WORLD

The ash fall formed a thick blanket throughout Eastern Washington, Northern Idaho and Western Montana varying in depths from one to six inches. The lower part of the plume, carried by lower altitude winds, swept northeastward across Washington and into Canada.

Higher altitude winds carried the ash southeast through the U.S. and eventually around the world.

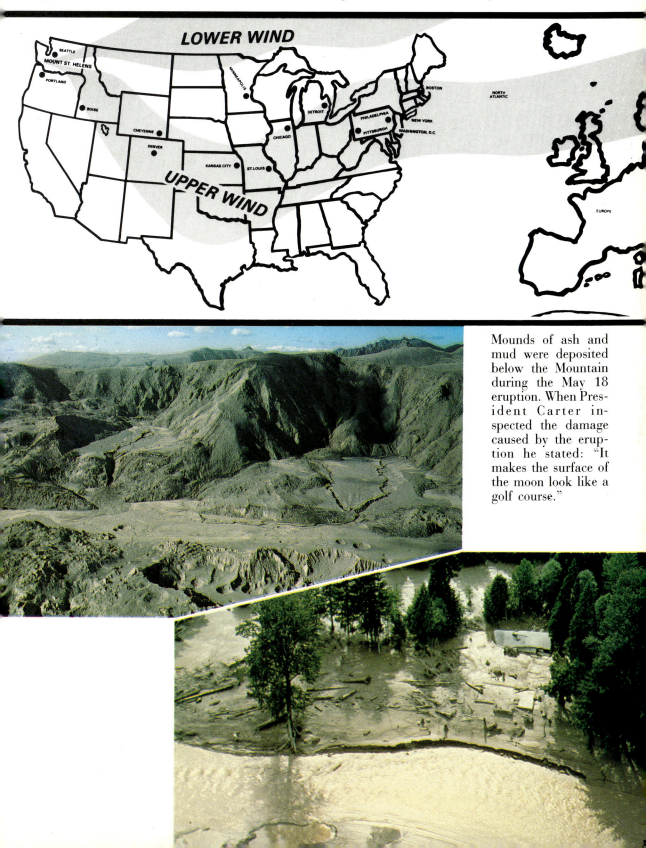

Mounds of ash and mud were deposited below the Mountain during the May 18 eruption. When President Carter inspected the damage caused by the eruption he stated: "It makes the surface of the moon look like a golf course."

BEFORE

AFTER

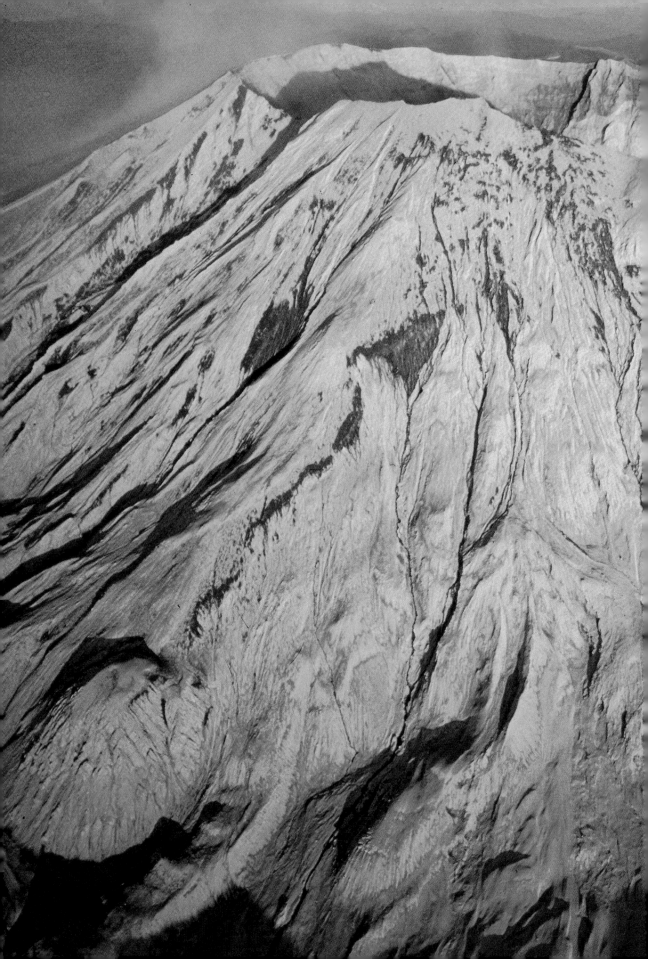

MOUNT ST. HELENS WITH MT. RAINIER IN DISTANCE
THE CASCADE RANGE IS A CHAIN OF POTENTIAL DANGER

CANADA

MT. BAKER GLACIER PEAK MT. ADAMS

MT. RAINIER MT. HOOD

SEATTLE

TACOMA MT. ST. HELENS

PUGET SOUND OLYMPIA

WASHINGTON PORTLAND WILLAMETTE EUGENE

COLUMBIA RIVER VALLEY OREGON

PACIFIC OCEAN

ERUPTED
260 YEARS AGO MT. LASSE
MT. SHASTA

McCLOUD
WEED DUNSMUIR
MOUNT
SHASTA

MEDFORD CALIFORNIA

CRESCENT CITY

MT. RAINIER   MT. ST. HELENS   MT. ADAMS

JULY 22, 1980

VIEWED FROM THE WILLAMETTE RIVER WHERE IT JOINS THE COLUMBIA RIVER

JULY 22, 1980

LAVA DOME CLOSE-UPS

The first sign of a lava dome, formed by the upward movement of magma slowly oozing out of the mountain and cooling, appeared on June 14. In four days it had grown to 280 feet in height and 660 feet in diameter. This first dome was destroyed by the July 22 eruption; since then new lava domes have formed following each major eruption, as nature attempts to rebuild a lost beauty.

MOLTON LAVA VISIBLE ▲

▼ STEAM RISING FROM LAVA DOME

WHAT CAUSES A VOLCANO!

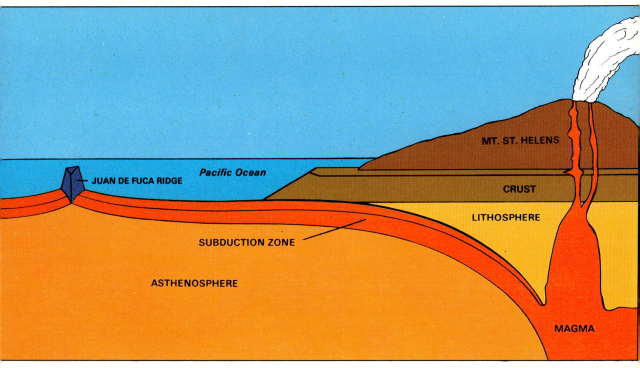

According to the theory of plate tectonics, the earth's crust, divided into 12 sections, called plates, floats atop the mantle. Each of the plates moves very slowly in relation to each other. Mt. St. Helens is the result of the Pacific plate, on which the Pacific Ocean rests, pushing up against the continental crust. The Pacific plate is pushed downward under the continental plate. As it is subducted, the tremendous heat and pressure that is generated work to melt the Pacific crust, forming a pool of magma. The magma then rises through any available crack, in this case a dormant volcano. When it reaches the surface a volcano is born, or rekindled.

NEW LIFE RETURNS TO A DEVASTATED AREA